The Night Before
Christmas

The Night Before Christmas

The Night Before
Christmas

Clement Clarke Moore
Illustrated by Tom Newsom

When out on the lawn
there arose such a clatter,
I sprang from the bed
to see what was the matter.

Away to the window
I flew like a flash,
Tore open the shutters,
and threw up the sash.

The moon on the breast
of the new-fallen snow
Gave the luster of midday
to objects below,

When, what to my wondering
eyes should appear,
But a miniature sleigh
and eight tiny reindeer,

With a little old driver,
so lively and quick,
I knew in a moment
it must be St. Nick.

More rapid than eagles
his coursers they came,
And he whistled, and shouted,
and called them by name:

As dry leaves that before
   the wild hurricane fly,
When they meet with an obstacle,
   mount to the sky,

So up to the housetop
   the coursers they flew,
With the sleigh full of toys,
   and St. Nicholas too.

And then, in a twinkling
I heard on the roof
The prancing and pawing
of each little hoof.

As I drew in my head,
and was turning around
Down the chimney St. Nicholas
came with a bound.

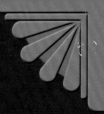

The stump of a pipe
   he held tight in his teeth,
And the smoke it encircled
   his head like a wreath.

He had a broad face
   and a little round belly
That shook when he laughed,
   like a bowlful of jelly.

He sprang to his sleigh,
  to his team gave a whistle,
And away they all flew
  like the down of a thistle.

But I heard him exclaim,
  ere he drove out of sight: